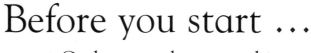

Before you start ...

1 Gather together everything you need for the activity using the equipment list at the top of each page. You can use PVA glue for all the activities in this book.

2 Cover your work table with newspaper and wear an apron to protect your clothes.

3 Read all the instructions carefully. Always wait for glue to dry.

4 Be very careful with scissors. Only use them if an adult is there to help you.

5 When you have finished an activity, wash your hands and put everything away.

DK

A DORLING KINDERSLEY BOOK

Written and edited by Lara Tankel and Dawn Sirett
Art Editors Mandy Earey and Mary Sandberg
Additional design Veneta Altham
Deputy Managing Art Editor C. David Gillingwater
Production Fiona Baxter and Jo Blackmore
Dib, Dab, and Dob made by Wilfrid Wood
Photography by Alex Wilson and Norman Hollands
Illustrations by Peter Kavanagh
Frieze, masks, dragon, and collage made by Jane Bull

First published in Great Britain in 1997
by Dorling Kindersley Limited,
9 Henrietta Street, London WC2E 8PS

Copyright © 1997 Dorling Kindersley Limited, London

Visit us on the World Wide Web at http://www.dk.com

A CIP catalogue record for this book is available from the British Library.

ISBN 0-7513-5569-0

Colour reproduction by Colourscan, Singapore
Printed and bound in Hong Kong by Imago

PLAY AND LEARN
Sticking things

With Dib, Dab, and Dob

DORLING KINDERSLEY

London • New York • Stuttgart • Moscow

black paper  scissors cellophane sweet wrappers PVA glue

Make stained-glass pictures

Ask an adult to fold a square of paper into four and to cut out shapes along the folded edges.

Fold the paper again and cut out more shapes.

Finally, open up the paper and glue sweet wrappers over all the holes.

Sprinkle glitter fish on a frieze

Draw some fish, waves, and seaweed on a long strip of card.

Carefully spread glue along the lines you have drawn.

Then sprinkle glitter over the glue.

flowers and leaves notebook PVA glue paintbrush

Cover a notebook with flowers

Stick flowers and leaves on to the front of a notebook with PVA glue.

Brush the glue all over the notebook and over the flowers and leaves, too.

felt-tip pen   card   felt   PVA glue   scissors

Design happy animal masks

Draw an oval mask with eyeholes on some card. Stick felt to the card and then cut round the mask.

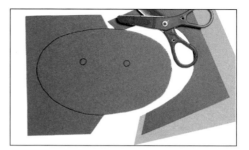

Cut out the eyeholes. Check that you can see through them.

tape   elastic

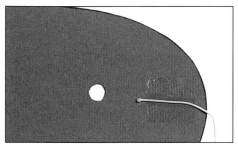

Tape the ends of a length of elastic to the back of the mask on each side.

I've made frog eyes by sticking felt pieces on to card.

Then stick on felt pieces to make an animal face.

Funny felt faces

Try making lots of masks for all
your friends to wear at a party.

paper pencil magazine PVA glue  tissue paper

Glue scales on a fiery dragon

Draw a dragon on some paper.

Choose pages from a magazine. Tear them into small squares and glue them on to the dragon.

Make a farm collage

Find things that you can use to make a farm picture. Cut them into the shapes you want.

Arrange them on a sheet of card.

card   PVA glue

Then glue the
things on to
the card.

Feely farm picture

Stick strips of card around the edge of the picture to make a frame.

The cotton wool sheep feel soft and fluffy. The bark feels bumpy and rough.